Way To Blue

AN INTRODUCTION TO NICK DRAKE

Exclusive Distributors:
Music Sales Limited, 8/9 Frith Street, London W1V 5TZ, England.
Music Sales Pty Limited, 120 Rothschild Avenue, Rosebery, NSW 2018, Australia.

Order No. AM958452. ISBN 0-7119-8179-5
This book © Copyright 2000 by Wise Publications.

Music arranged by James Dean. Edited by Arthur Dick. Music processed by Andrew Shiels.

Your Guarantee of Quality:
As publishers, we strive to produce every book to the highest commercial standards.
The music has been freshly engraved and, whilst endeavouring to retain the original running order of the recorded album,
the book has been carefully designed to minimise awkward page turns and to make playing from it a real pleasure.
Throughout, the printing and binding have been planned to ensure a sturdy, attractive publication which should give years of enjoyment.
If your copy fails to meet our high standards, please inform us and we will gladly replace it.

Music Sales' complete catalogue describes thousands of titles and is available in full colour sections by subject,
direct from Music Sales Limited. Please state your areas of interest and send a cheque/postal order for £1.50 for postage to:
Music Sales Limited, Newmarket Road, Bury St. Edmunds, Suffolk IP33 3YB.

www.musicsales.com

This publication is not authorised for sale in
the United States of America and/or Canada

Wise Publications
London/New York/Paris/Sydney/Copenhagen/Madrid/Tokyo

Guitar Tablature Explained

Guitar music can be notated three different ways: on a musical stave, in tablature, and in rhythm slashes

RHYTHM SLASHES are written above the stave. Strum chords in the rhythm indicated. Round noteheads indicate single notes.

THE MUSICAL STAVE shows pitches and rhythms and is divided by lines into bars. Pitches are named after the first seven letters of the alphabet.

TABLATURE graphically represents the guitar fingerboard. Each horizontal line represents a string, and each number represents a fret.

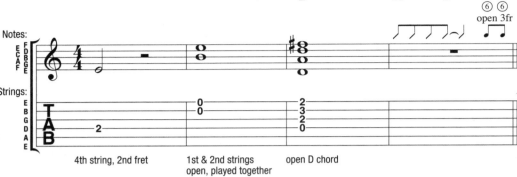

4th string, 2nd fret — 1st & 2nd strings open, played together — open D chord

Definitions for special guitar notation

SEMI-TONE BEND: Strike the note and bend up a semi-tone (1/2 step).

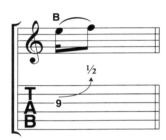

WHOLE-TONE BEND: Strike the note and bend up a whole-tone (whole step).

GRACE NOTE BEND: Strike the note and bend as indicated. Play the first note as quickly as possible.

QUARTER-TONE BEND: Strike the note and bend up a 1/4 step.

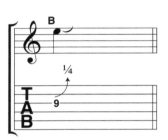

BEND & RELEASE: Strike the note and bend up as indicated, then release back to the original note.

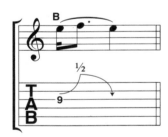

BEND & RESTRIKE: Strike the note and bend as indicated then restrike the string where the symbol occurs.

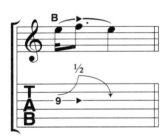

PRE-BEND: Bend the note as indicated, then strike it.

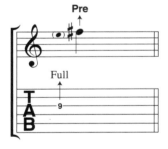

PRE-BEND & RELEASE: Bend the note as indicated. Strike it and release the note back to the original pitch.

HAMMER-ON: Strike the first (lower) note with one finger, then sound the higher note (on the same string) with another finger by fretting it without picking.

PULL-OFF: Place both fingers on the notes to be sounded. Strike the first note and without picking, pull the finger off to sound the second (lower) note.

LEGATO SLIDE (GLISS): Strike the first note and then slide the same fret-hand finger up or down to the second note. The second note is not struck.

SHIFT SLIDE (GLISS & RESTRIKE): Same as legato slide, except the second note is struck.

NATURAL HARMONIC: Strike the note while the fret-hand lightly touches the string directly over the fret indicated.

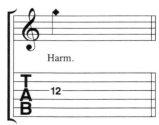

PICK SCRAPE: The edge of the pick is rubbed down (or up) the string, producing a scratchy sound.

PALM MUTING: The note is partially muted by the pick hand lightly touching the string(s) just before the bridge.

MUFFLED STRINGS: A percussive sound is produced by laying the fret hand across the string(s) without depressing, and striking them with the pick hand.

NOTE: The speed of any bend is indicated by the music notation and tempo.

Way To Blue

Words & Music by Nick Drake

Standard tuning

Intro

Freely ♩=66

Strings arranged for guitar

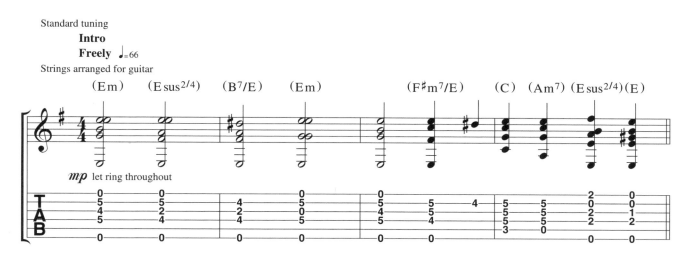

Verse

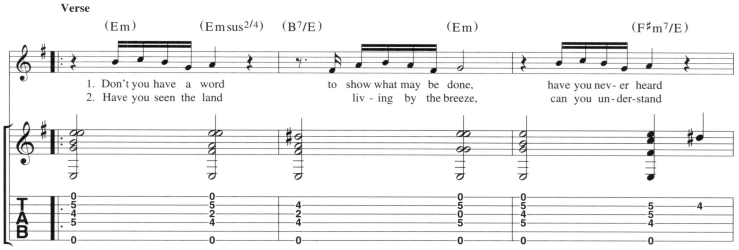

1. Don't you have a word to show what may be done, have you nev-er heard
2. Have you seen the land liv - ing by the breeze, can you un-der-stand

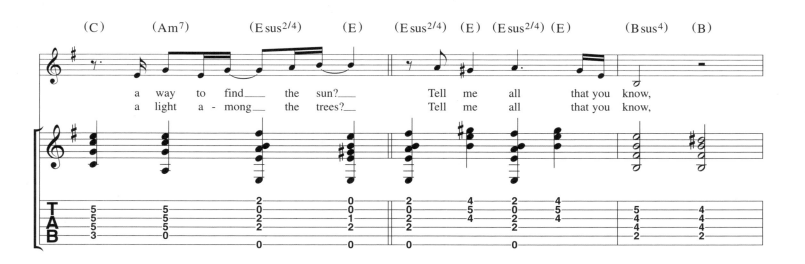

a way to find___ the sun?___ Tell me all that you know,
a light a - mong___ the trees?___ Tell me all that you know,

4

Verse

3. Can you now re-call all that you have known,— will you nev-er fall— when the light has flown. Tell me all that you know, show me what you have to show. Won't you come and say if you know the way to blue.

Cello Song

Words & Music by Nick Drake

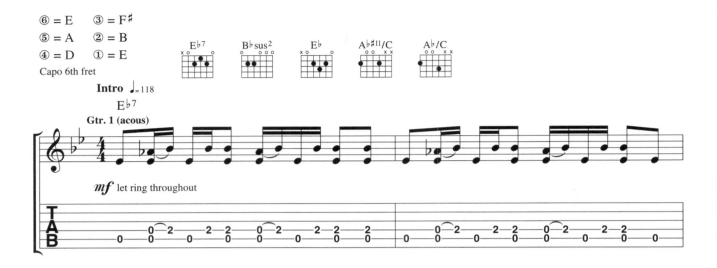

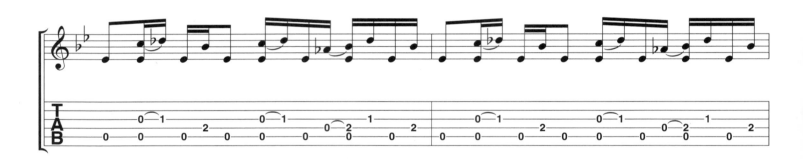

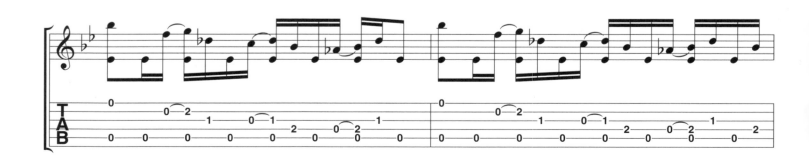

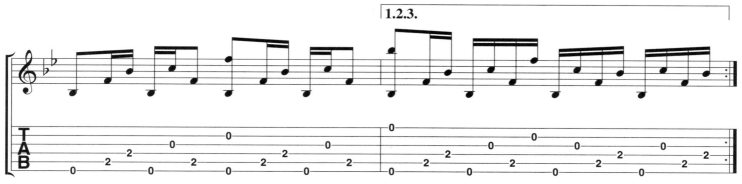

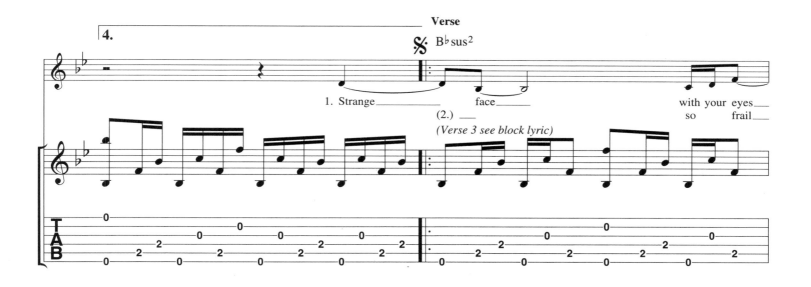

Verse

1. Strange_____ face_____ with your eyes_____

(2.) ____ so frail_____

(Verse 3 see block lyric)

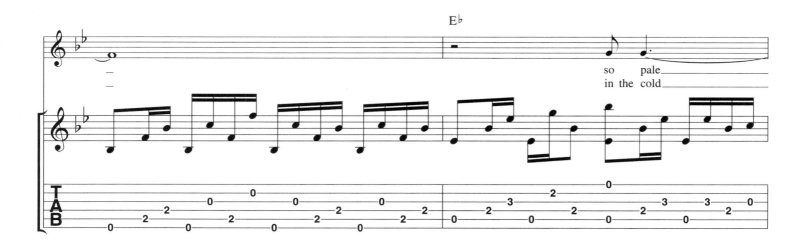

so pale_____

in the cold_____

7

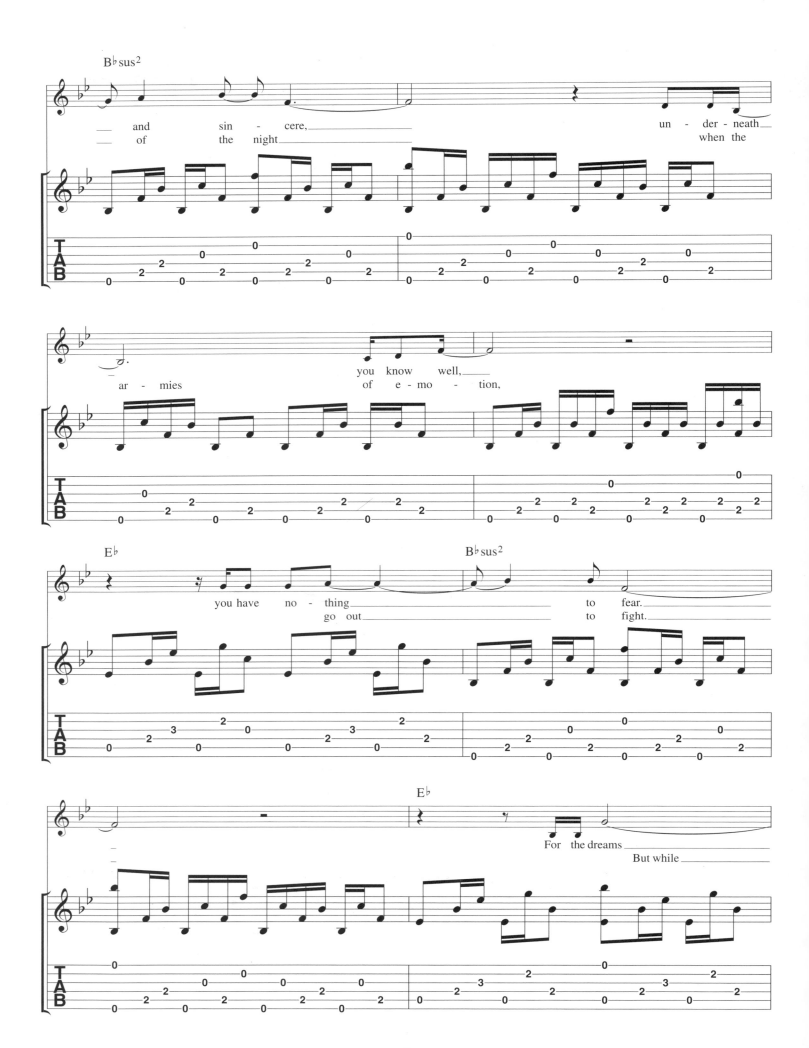

Verse 3:

So forget this cruel world
Where I belong
I'll just sit and wait
And sing my song
And if one day you should see me in the crowd
Lend a hand and lift me
To your place in the cloud.

11

Hazey Jane I

Words & Music by Nick Drake

Verse 3:   Can you tell me if you're moving
With no mirror to see
If you're just riding a new man
That looks a little like me.
Is it all so confusing?
Is it hard to believe?
When the winter is coming
Can you sign up and leave?

Chorus 3:   Hey slow, Jane, live your lie
Slow, slow, Jane, fly on by.

Things Behind The Sun

Words & Music by Nick Drake

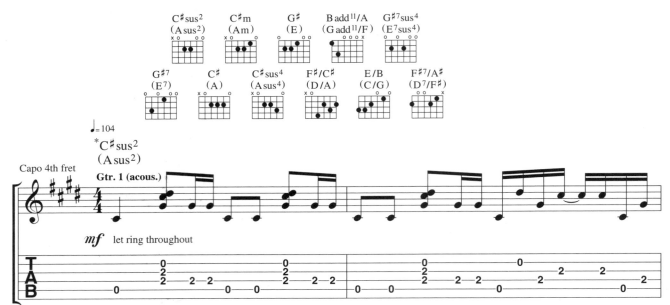

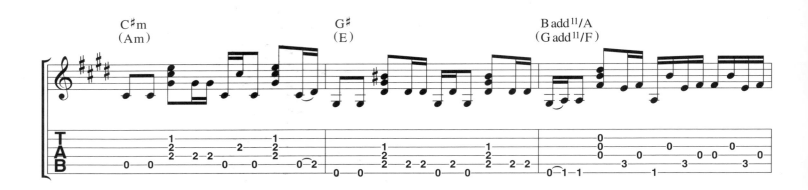

* Symbols in parentheses represent chord names with respect to capoed gtr. (Tab 0 = 4th fret)
Symbols above represent actual sounding chords.

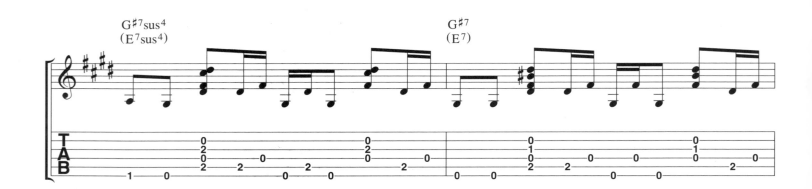

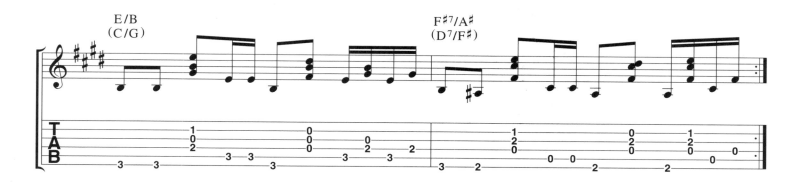

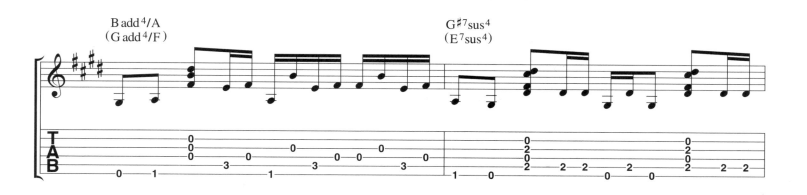

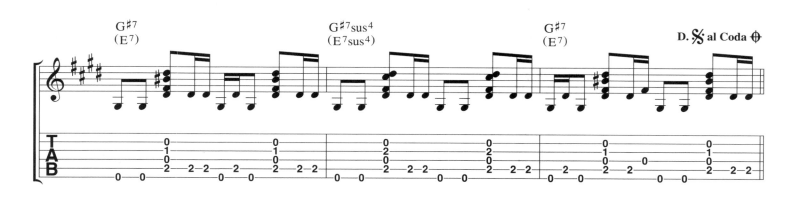

⊕ Coda

But say what you'll _____ say

River Man

Words & Music by Nick Drake

26

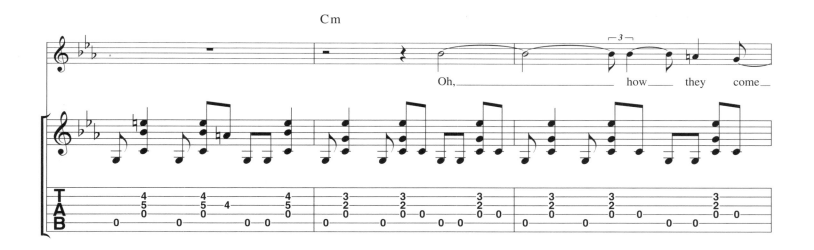

Cm

Oh,_____ how___ they come_

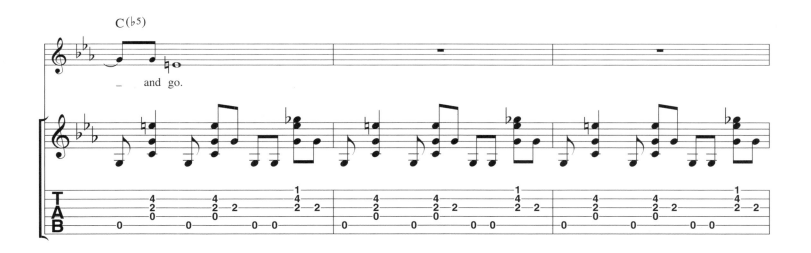

C(♭5)

_ and go.

to fade

Verse 3:

Betty said she prayed today
For the sky to blow away
Or maybe stay
She wasn't sure.
For when she thought of summer rain
Calling for her mind again
She lost the pain
And stayed for more.

Verse 4:

Going to see the river man
Going to tell him all I can
About the ban
On feeling free.
If he tells me all he knows
About the way his river flows
I don't suppose
It's meant for me.

Poor Boy

Words & Music by Nick Drake

count your___ coins___ and throw them ov - - - er___ my shoul -
things I___ say___ may seem stran - ger than

- der, I may___ grow old -er.
Sun - day, chang - ing___ to Mon-day.

Bridge

1.(%) No - bod - y knows,___ how cold it grows,___
2. No - bod - y knows,___ how cold it flows,___

Gtr 2. w/Rhy. Fig. 1

and no - bod - y sees,___ how sha - ky my___ knees.
and no - bod - y feels,___ the worn down___ heels

35

Time Of No Reply

Words & Music by Nick Drake

39

From The Morning

Words & Music by Nick Drake

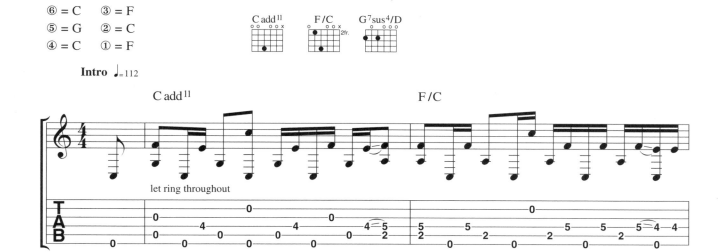

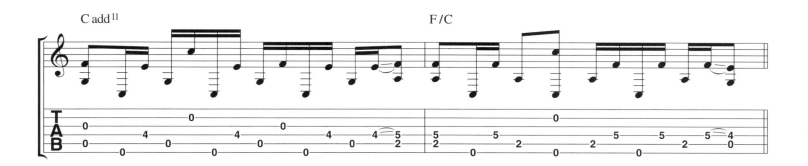

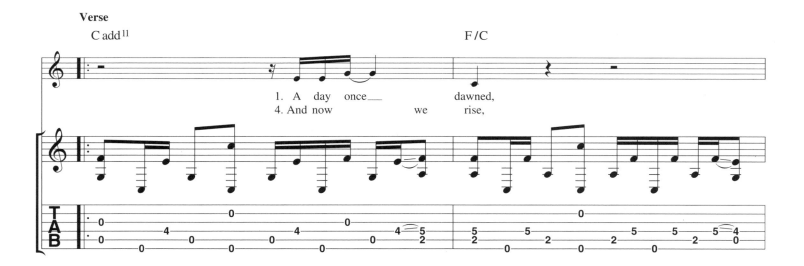

1. A day once dawned,
4. And now we rise,

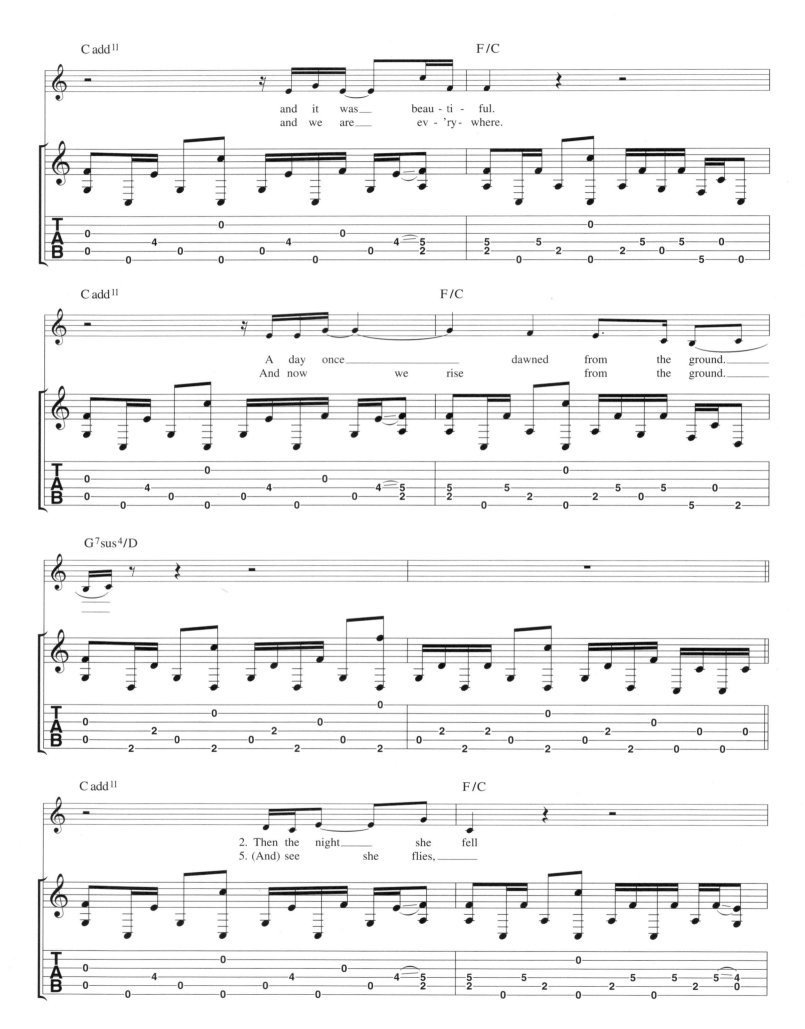

and it was___ beau-ti-ful.
and we are___ ev-'ry-where.

A day once_____ dawned from the ground.___
And now___ we rise from the ground.___

2. Then the night___ she fell
5. (And) see she flies, ___

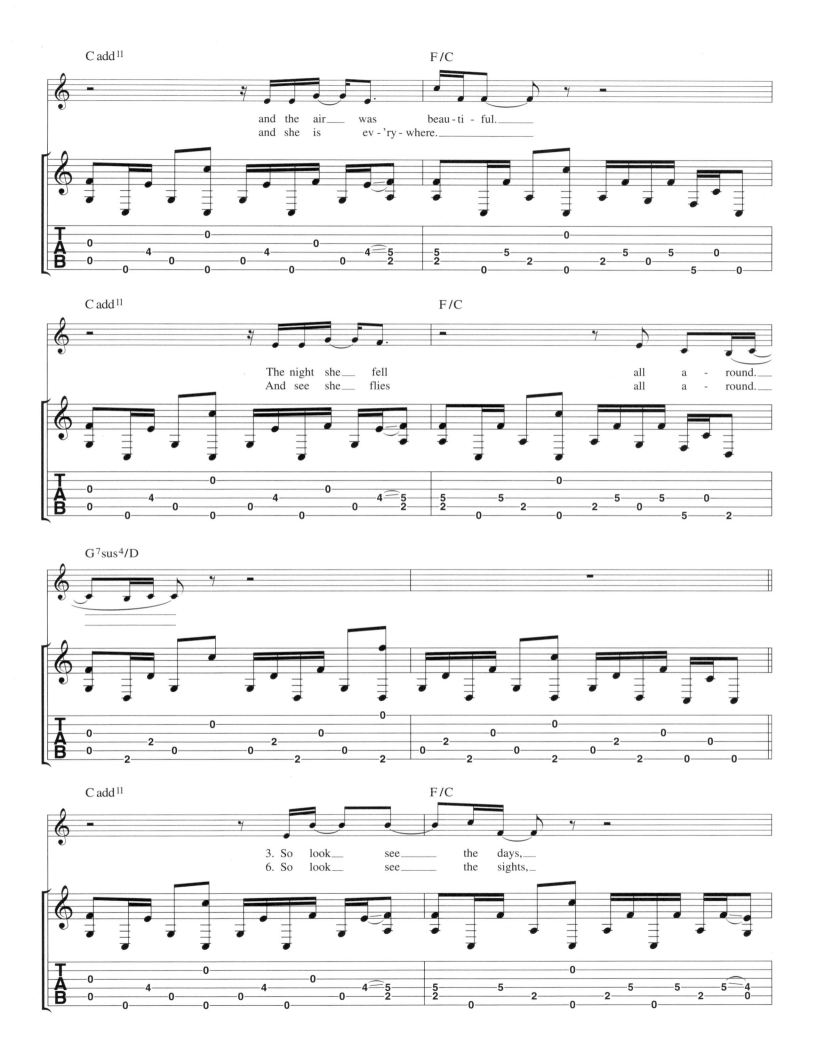

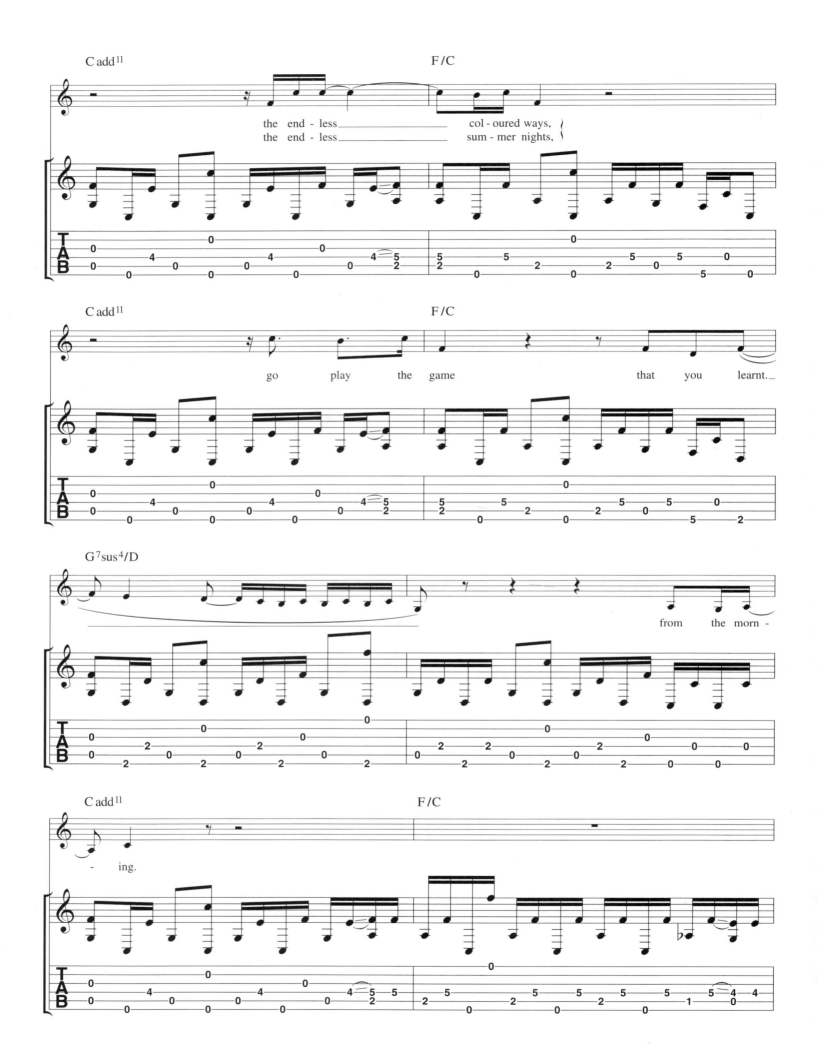

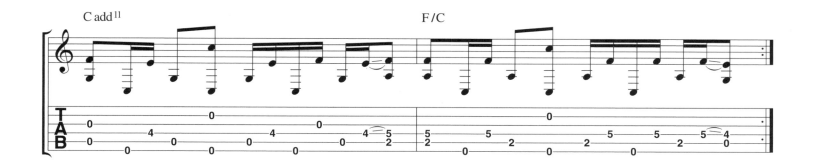

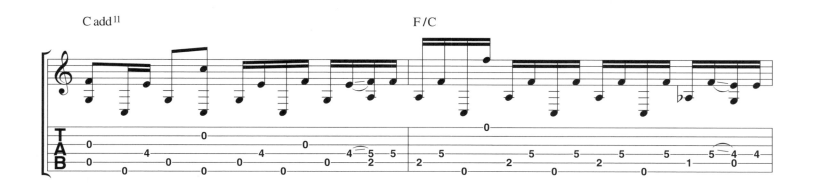

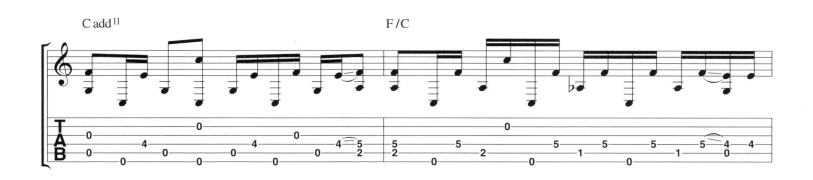

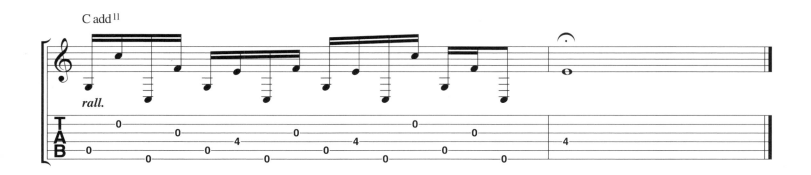

One Of These Things First

Words & Music by Nick Drake

47

49

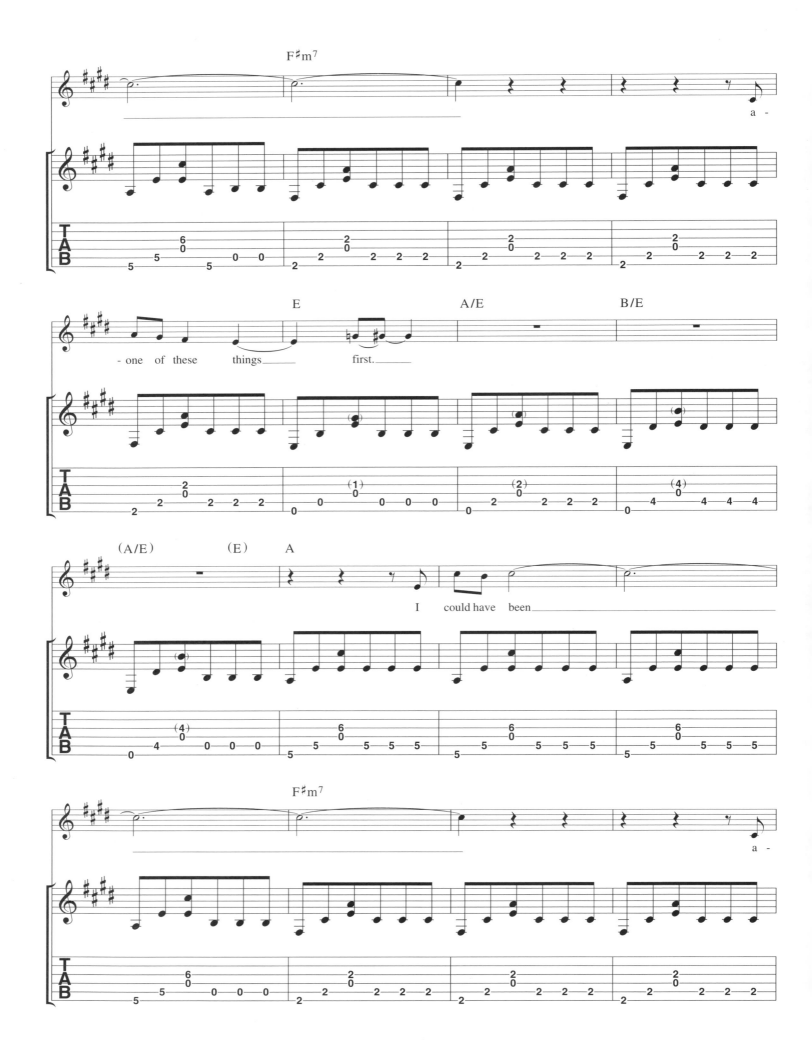

50

- one of these things_____ first._____

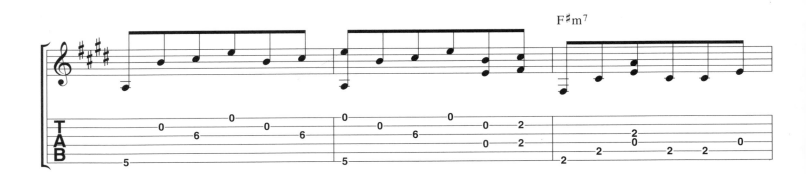

⊕ Coda

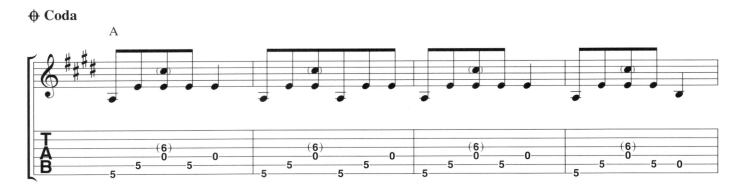

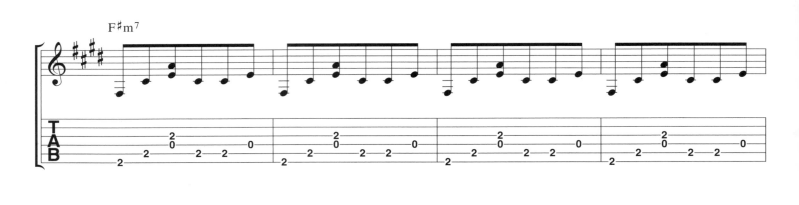

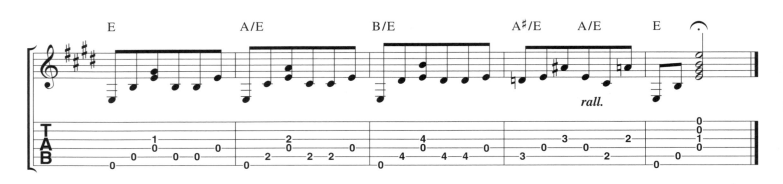

Northern Sky

Words & Music by Nick Drake

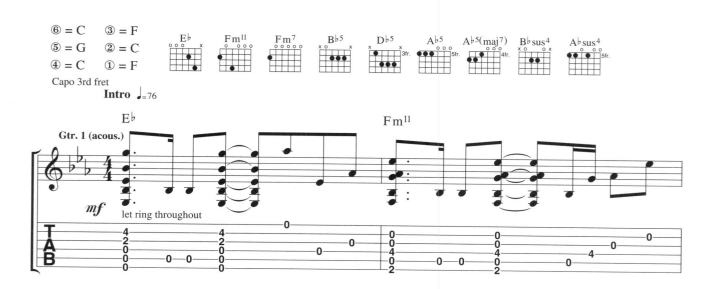

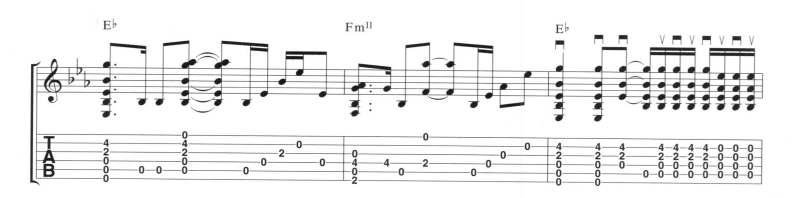

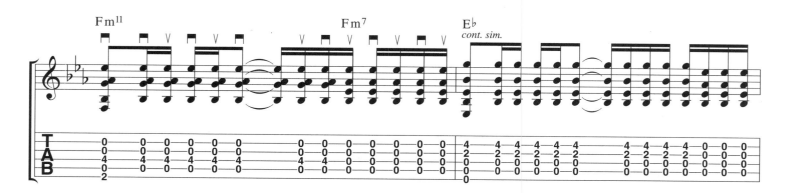

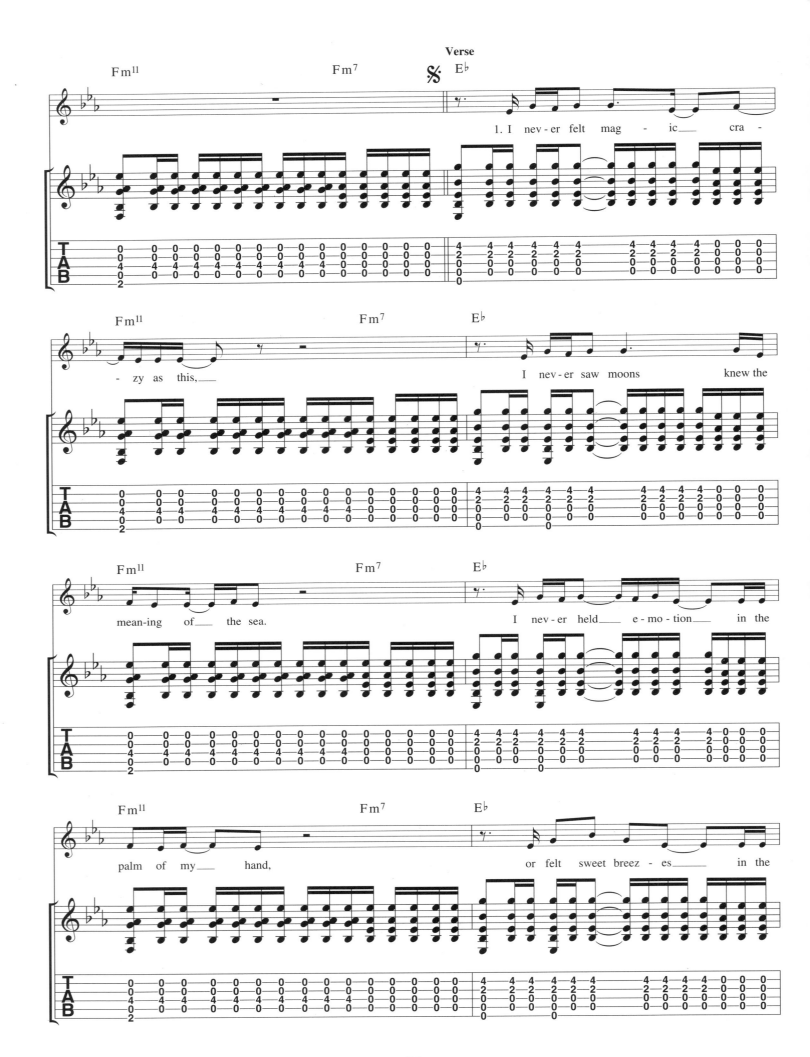

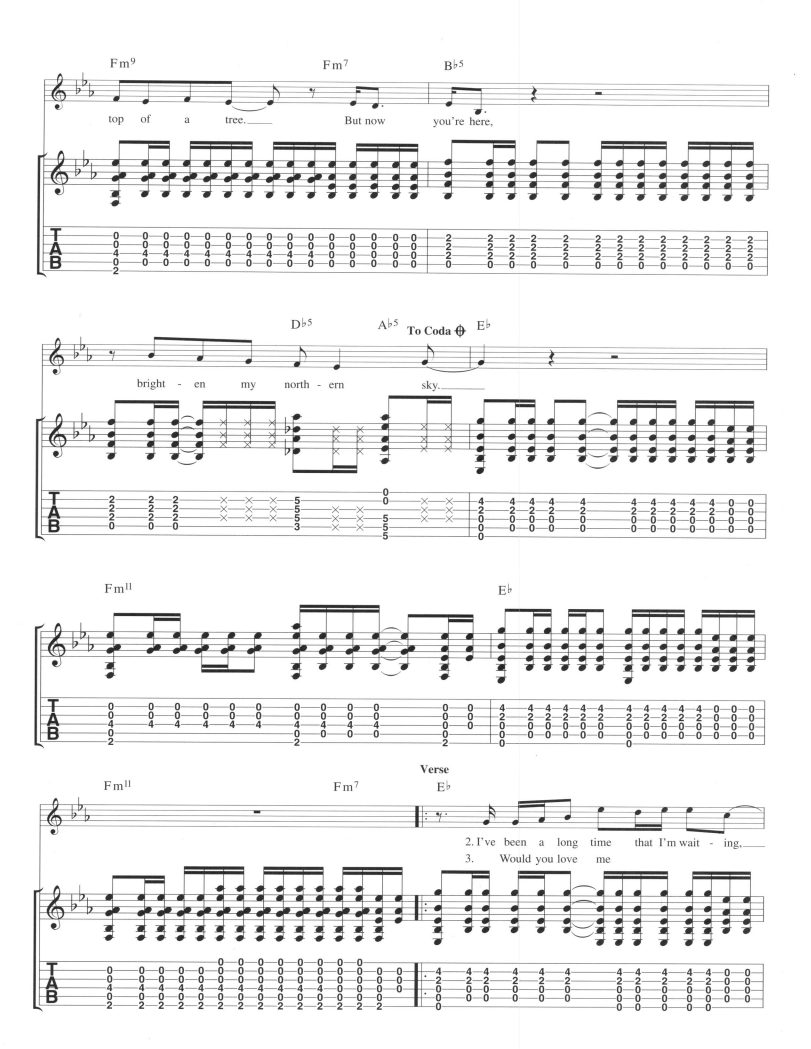

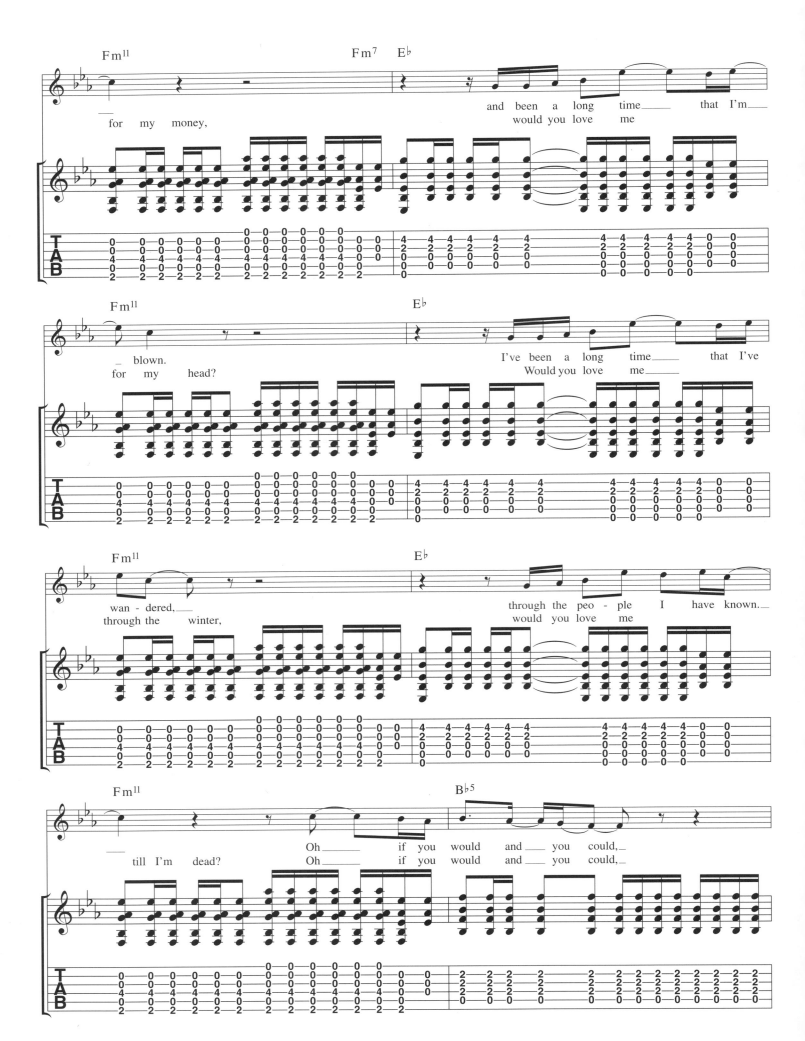

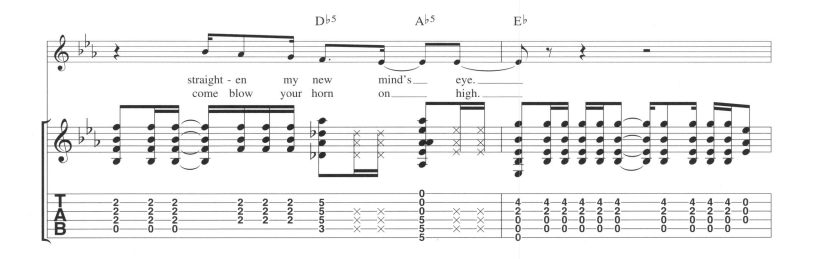

straight - en   my   new   mind's   eye.
come   blow   your   horn   on   high.

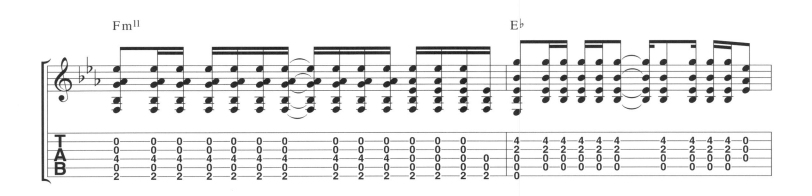

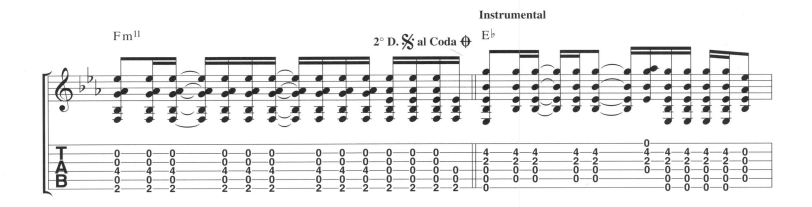

Instrumental

2° D. 𝄋 al Coda ⊕

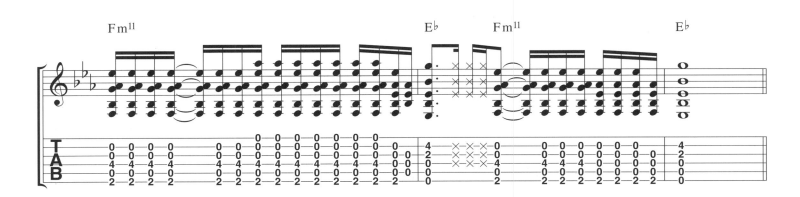

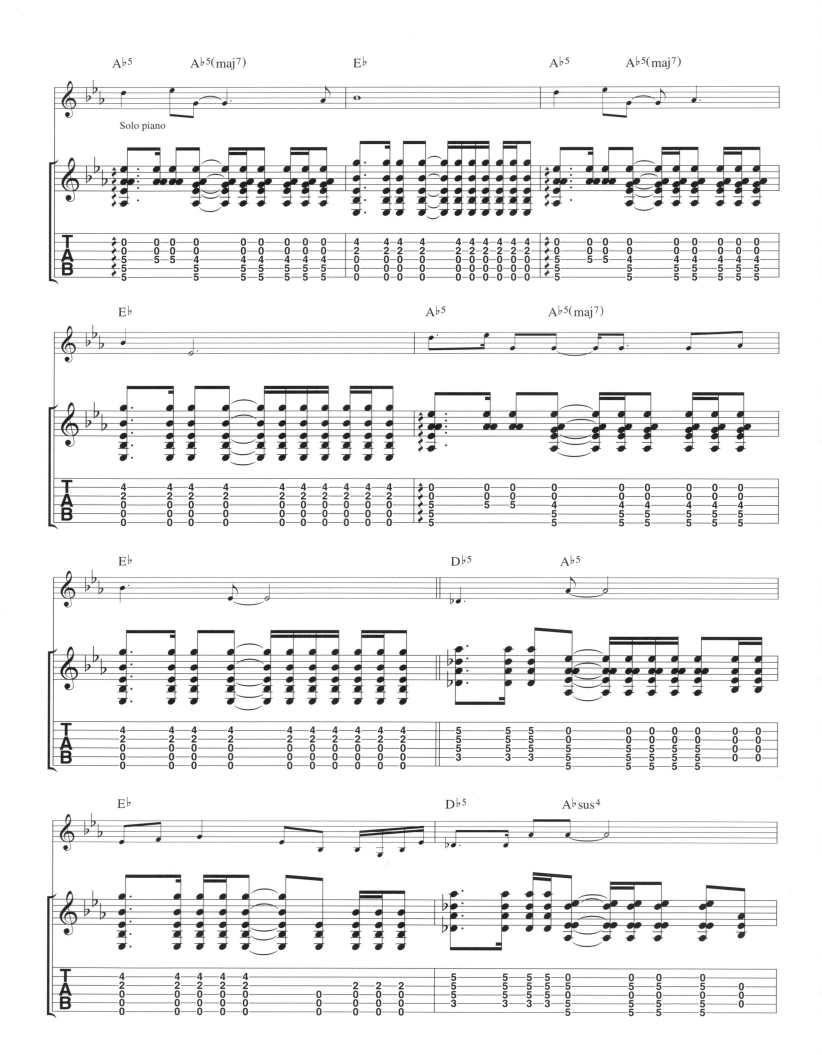

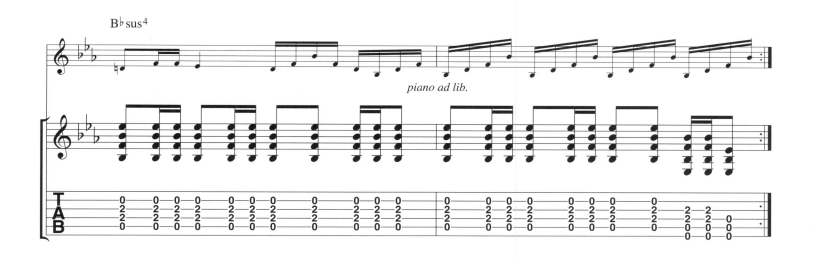

✠ Coda

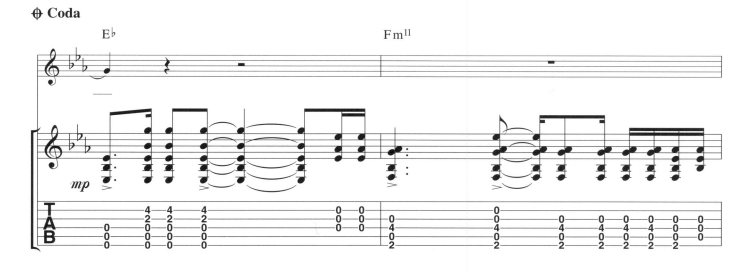

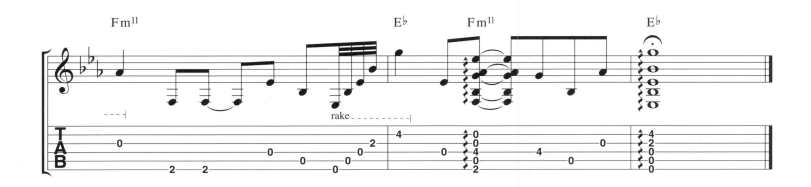

Which Will

Words & Music by Nick Drake

* Recording sounds slightly sharp. Tune sharp if necessary

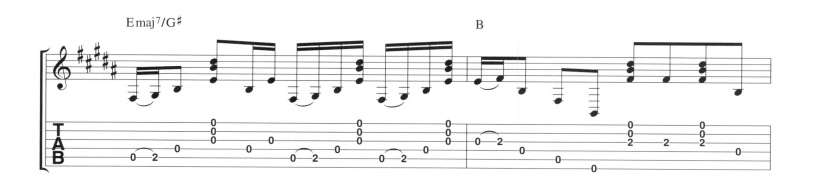

Verse

1. Which will_____ you go for,
2. Which do you dance for,

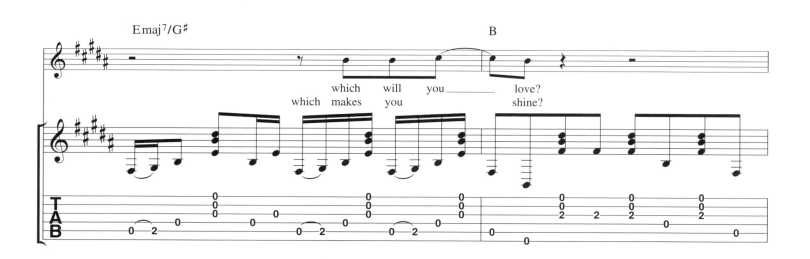

which will you_____ love?
which makes you shine?

61

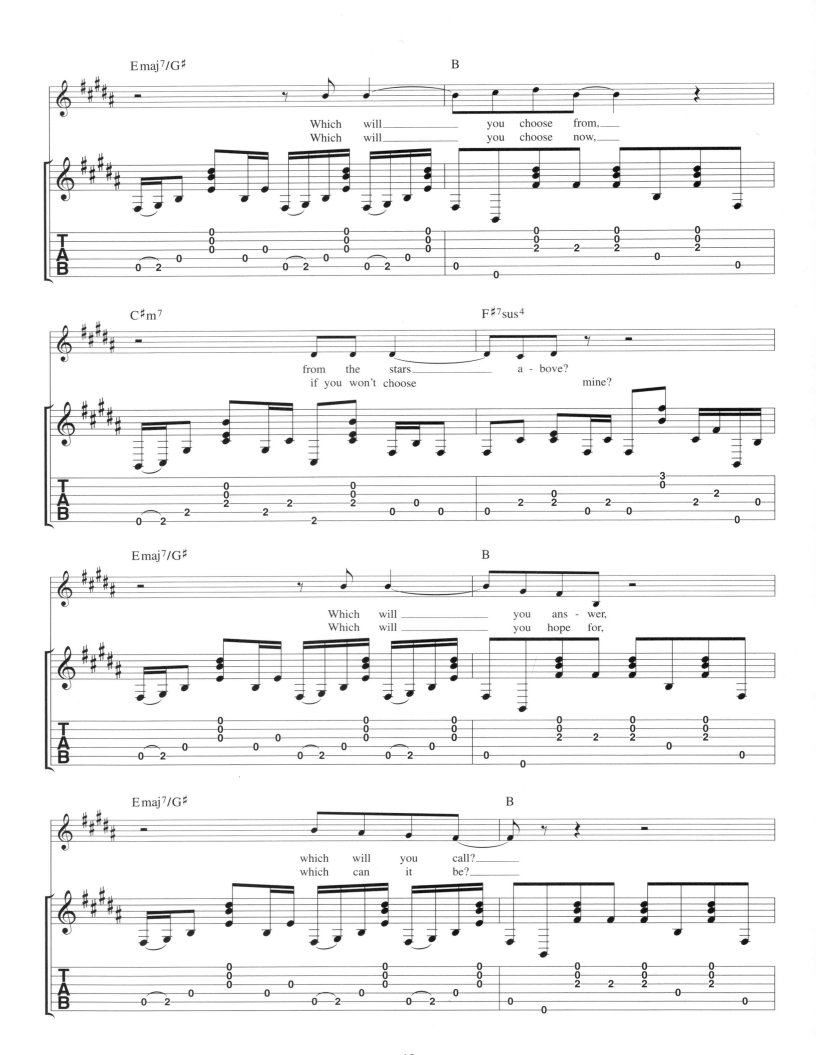

Time Has Told Me

Words & Music by Nick Drake

* Symbols in parentheses represent chord names with respect to capoed gtr. (Tab 0 = 3rd fret)
  Symbols above represent actual sounding chords.

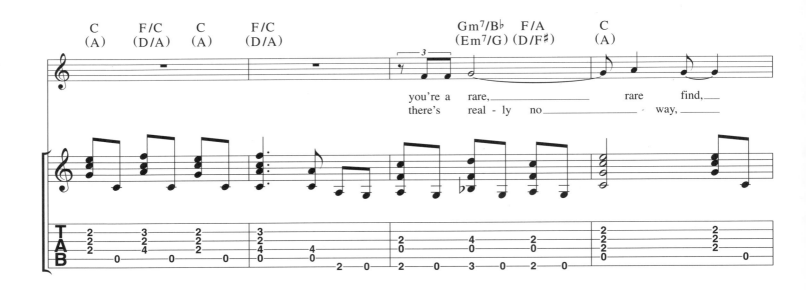

you're a rare, ___ rare find, ___
there's real-ly no ___ way, ___

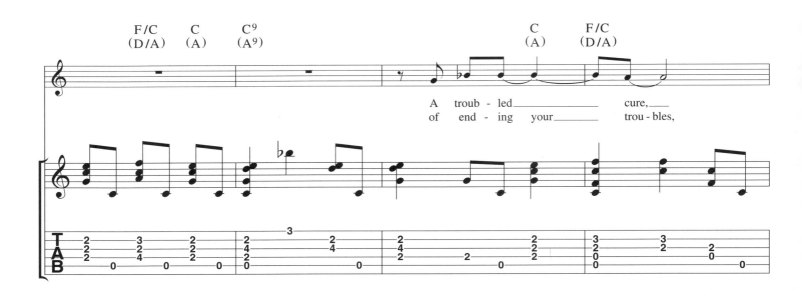

A troub-led ___ cure, ___
of end-ing your ___ trou-bles,

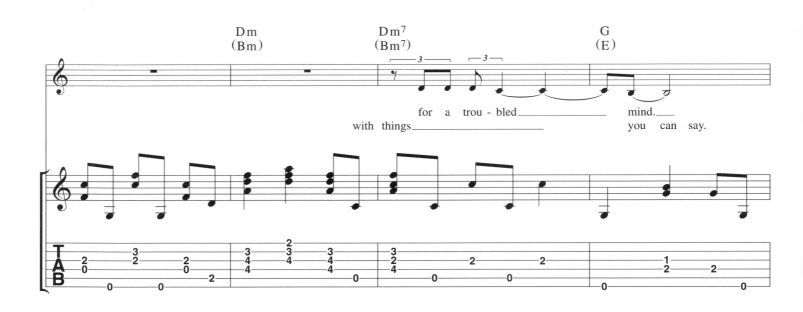

for a trou-bled ___ mind. ___
with things ___ you can say.

Bridge

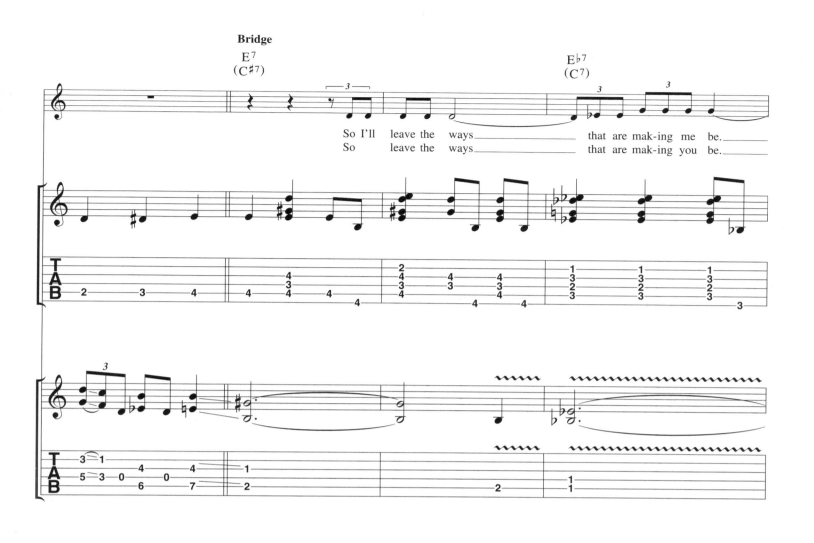

So I'll leave the ways_____ that are mak-ing me be.____
So leave the ways_____ that are mak-ing you be.____

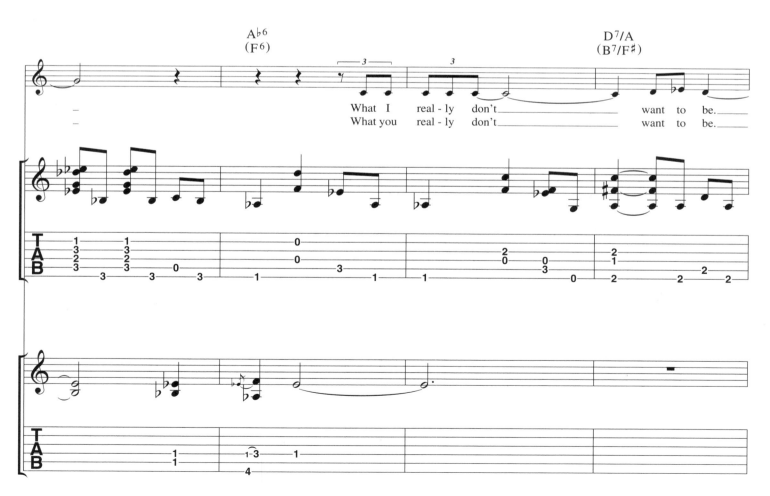

— What I real-ly don't_____ want to be.____
— What you real-ly don't_____ want to be.____

Leave the ways_____ that are mak-ing me love
Leave the ways_____ that are mak-ing you love

what I real - ly don't_____ want to love._____
what you real - ly don't_____ want to love._____

For some-day our_____ o - cean

will find_____ its shore.

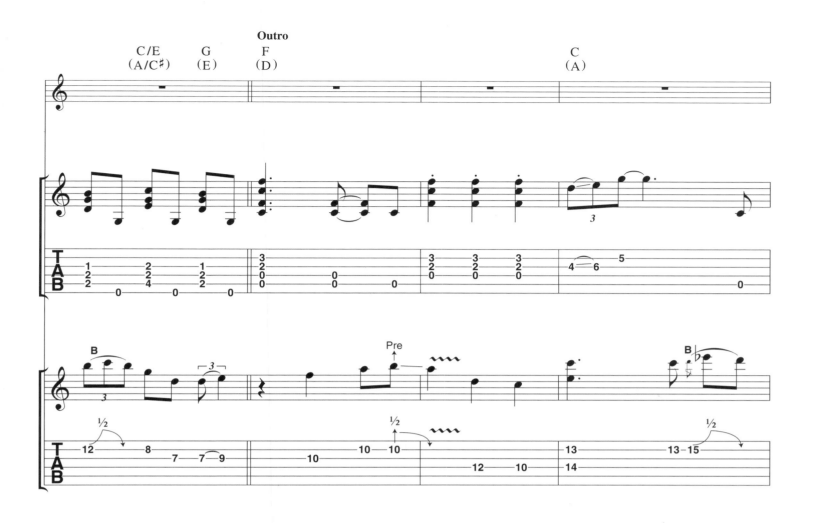

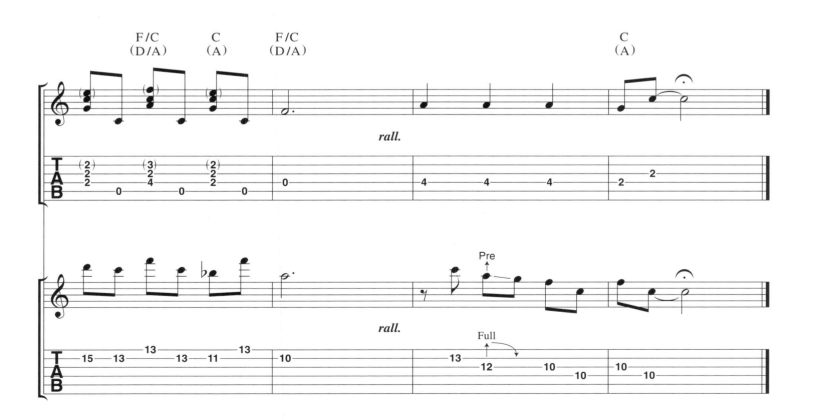

Pink Moon

Words & Music by Nick Drake

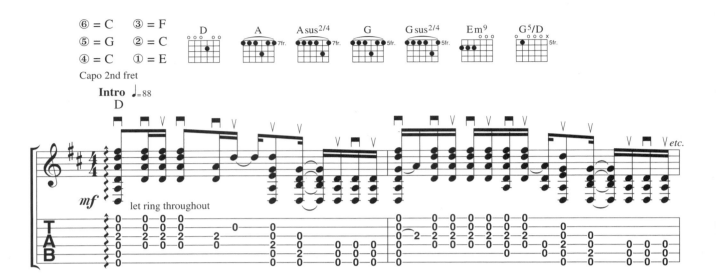

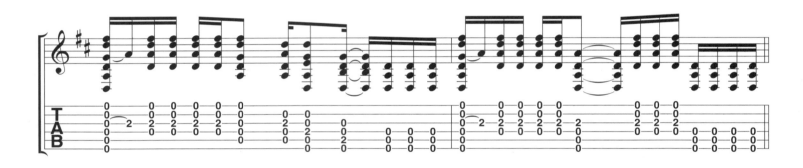

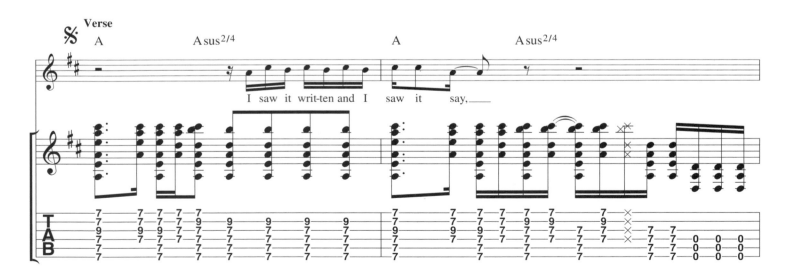

I saw it writ-ten and I saw it say,___

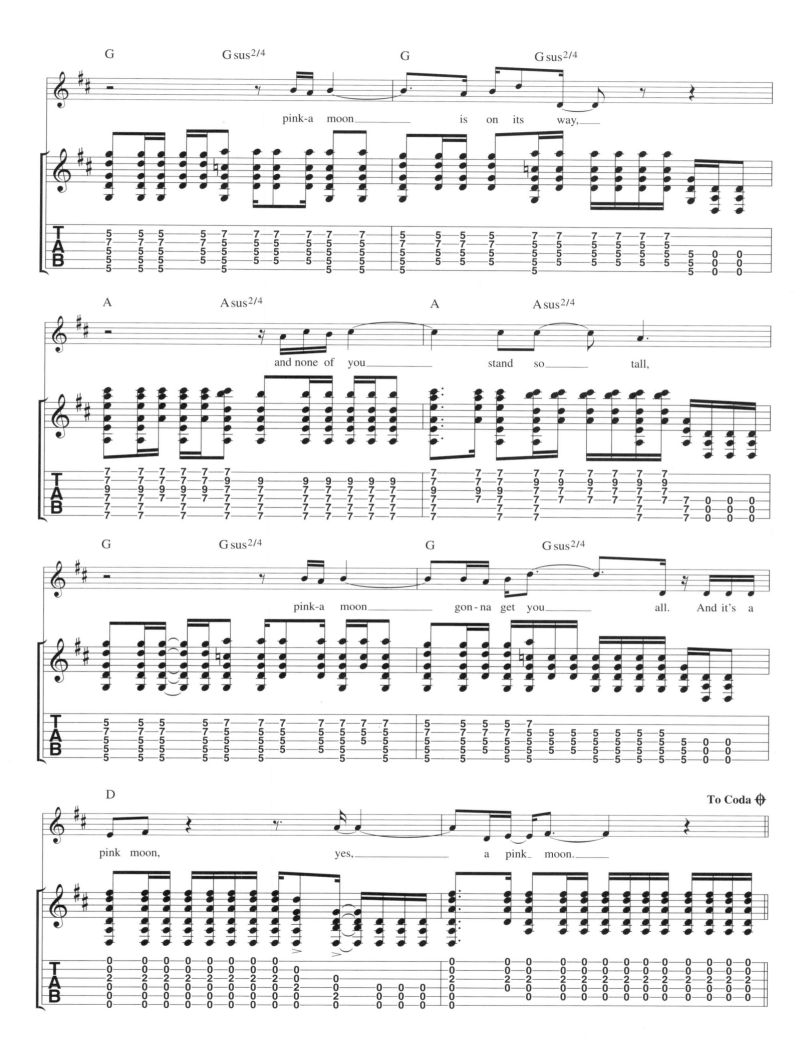

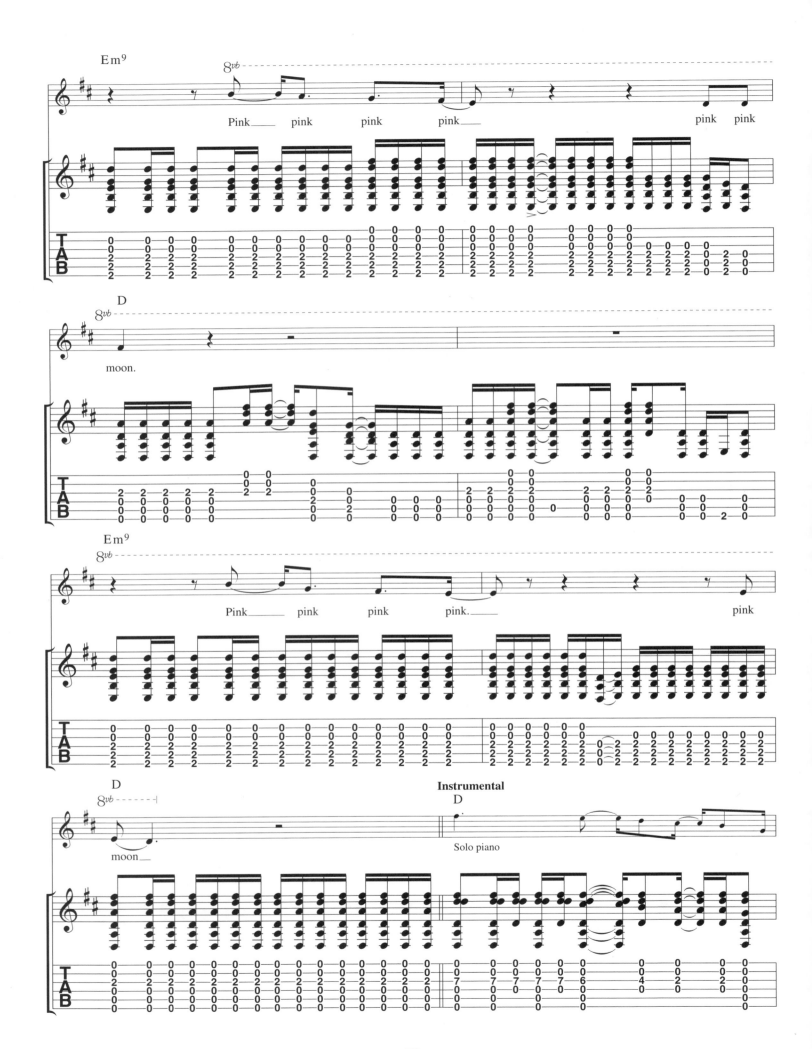

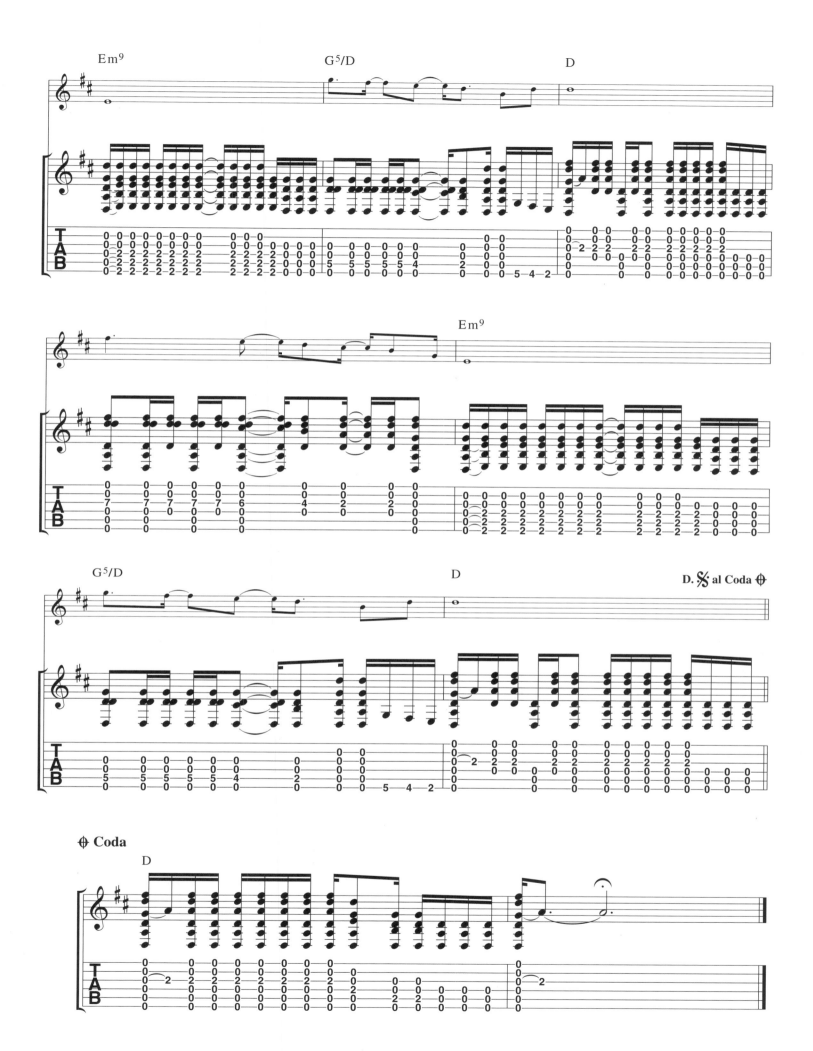

Black Eyed Dog

Words & Music by Nick Drake

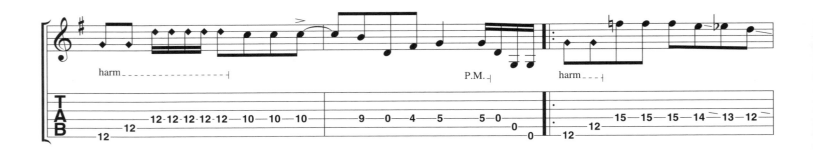

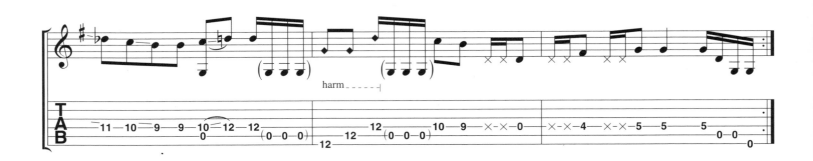

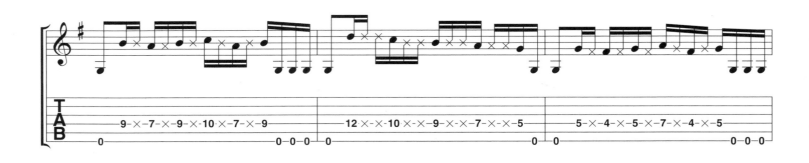

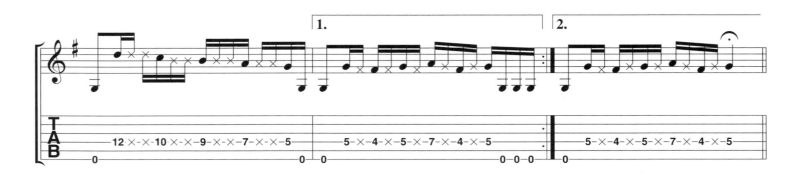

Verse

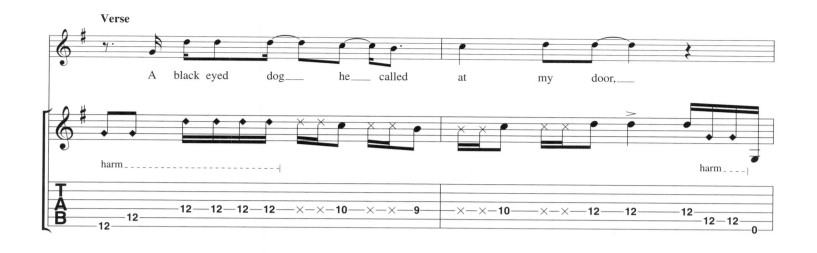

A black eyed dog___ he___ called at my door,___

A black eyed dog___ he___ called

for more.___

Fruit Tree

Words & Music by Nick Drake

91

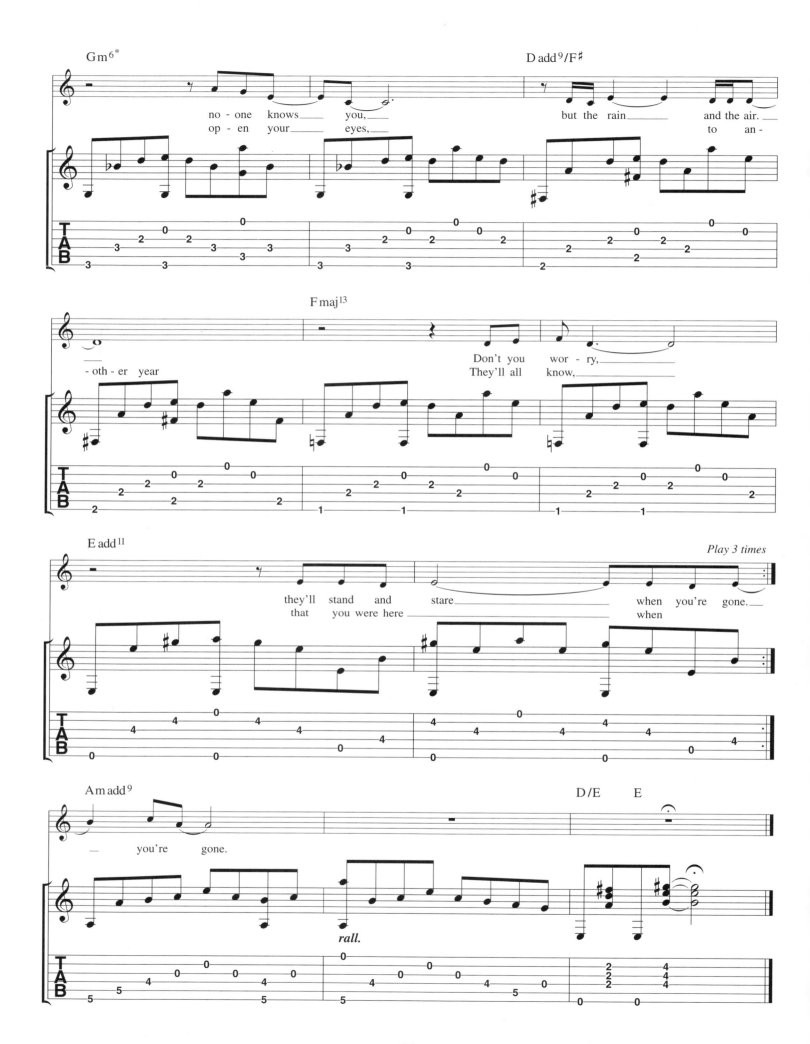

Présentation De La Tablature De Guitare

Il existe trois façons différentes de noter la musique pour guitare : à l'aide d'une portée musicale, de tablatures ou de barres rythmiques.

Les **BARRES RYTHMIQUES** sont indiquées au-dessus de la portée. Jouez les accords dans le rythme indiqué. Les notes rondes indiquent des notes réciles.

La **PORTÉE MUSICALE** indique les notes et rythmes et est divisée en mesures. Cette division est représentée par des lignes. Les notes sont : do, ré, mi, fa, sol, la, si.

La **PORTÉE EN TABLATURE** est une représentation graphique des touches de guitare. Chaque ligne horizontale correspond à une corde et chaque chiffre correspond à une case.

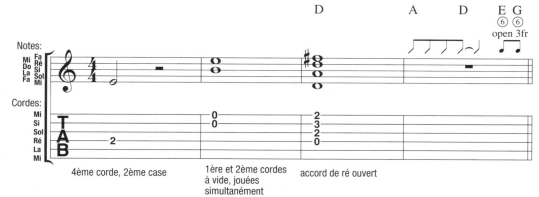

4ème corde, 2ème case   1ère et 2ème cordes à vide, jouées simultanément   accord de ré ouvert

Notation Spéciale De Guitare : Définitions

TIRÉ DEMI-TON : Jouez la note et tirez la corde afin d'élever la note d'un demi-ton (étape à moitié).

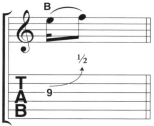

TIRÉ PLEIN : Jouez la note et tirez la corde afin d'élever la note d'un ton entier (étape entière).

TIRÉ D'AGRÉMENT : Jouez la note et tirez la corde comme indiqué. Jouez la première note aussi vite que possible.

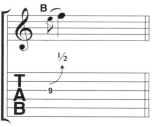

TIRÉ QUART DE TON : Jouez la note et tirez la corde afin d'élever la note d'un quart de ton.

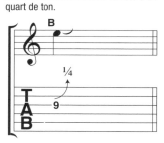

TIRÉ ET LÂCHÉ : Jouez la note et tirez la corde comme indiqué, puis relâchez, afin d'obtenir de nouveau la note de départ.

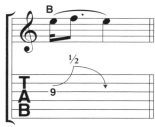

TIRÉ ET REJOUÉ : Jouez la note et tirez la corde comme indiqué puis rejouez la corde où le symbole apparaît.

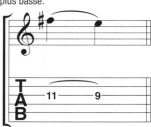

PRÉ-TIRÉ : Tirez la corde comme indiqué puis jouez cette note.

PRÉ-TIRÉ ET LÂCHÉ : Tirez la corde comme indiqué. Jouez la note puis relâchez la corde afin d'obtenir le ton de départ.

HAMMER-ON: Jouez la première note (plus basse) avec un doigt puis jouez la note plus haute sur la même corde avec un autre doigt, sur le manche mais sans vous servir du médiator.

PULL-OFF: Positionnez deux doigts sur les notes à jouer. Jouez la première note et sans vous servir du médiator, dégagez un doigt pour obtenir la deuxième note, plus basse.

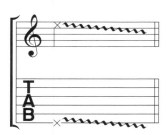

GLISSANDO : Jouez la première note puis faites glisser le doigt le long du manche pour obtenir la seconde note qui, elle, n'est pas jouée.

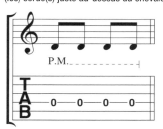

GLISSANDO ET REJOUÉ : Identique au glissando à ceci près que la seconde note est jouée.

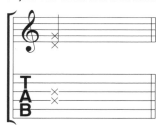

HARMONIQUES NATURELLES : Jouez la note tandis qu'un doigt effleure la corde sur le manche correspondant à la case indiquée.

PICK SCRAPE (SCRATCH) : On fait glisser le médiator le long de la corde, ce qui produit un son éraillé.

ÉTOUFFÉ DE LA PAUME : La note est partiellement étouffée par la main (celle qui se sert du médiator). Elle effleure la (les) corde(s) juste au-dessus du chevalet.

CORDES ÉTOUFFÉES : Un effet de percussion produit en posant à plat la main sur le manche sans relâcher, puis en jouant les cordes avec le médiator.

NOTE: La vitesse des tirés est indiquée par la notation musicale et le tempo.

Erläuterung zur Tabulaturschreibweise

Es gibt drei Möglichkeiten, Gitarrenmusik zu notieren: im klassichen Notensystem, in Tabulaturform oder als rhythmische Akzente.

RHYTHMISCHE AKZENTE werden über dem Notensystem notiert. Geschlagene Akkorde werden rhythmisch dargestellt. Ausgeschriebene Noten stellen Einzeltöne dar.

Im **NOTENSYSTEM** werden Tonhöhe und rhythmischer Verlauf festgelegt; es ist durch Taktstriche in Takte unterteilt. Die Töne werden nach den ersten acht Buchstaben des Alphabets benannt.
Beachte: "B" in der anglo-amerkanischen Schreibweise entspricht dem deutschen "H"!

DIE TABULATUR ist die optische Darstellung des Gitarrengriffbrettes. Jeder horizontalen Linie ist eine bestimmte Saite zugeordnet, jede Zahl bezeichnet einen Bund.

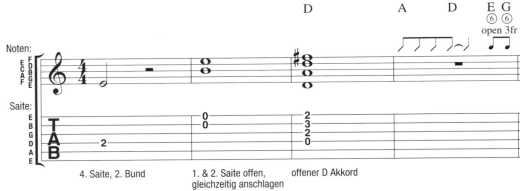

4. Saite, 2. Bund   1. & 2. Saite offen,   offener D Akkord
                     gleichzeitig anschlagen

Erklärungen zur speziellen Gitarennotation

HALBTON-ZIEHER: Spiele die Note und ziehe dann um einen Halbton höher (Halbtonschritt).

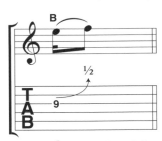

GANZTON-ZIEHER: Spiele die Note und ziehe dann einen Ganzton höher (Ganztonschritt).

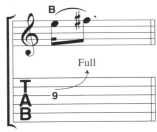

ZIEHER MIT VORSCHLAG: Spiele die Note und ziehe wie notiert. Spiele die erste Note so schnell wie möglich.

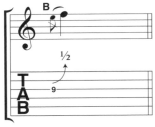

VIERTELTON-ZIEHER: Spiele die Note und ziehe dann einen Viertelton höher (Vierteltonschritt).

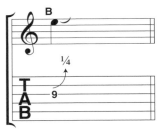

ZIEHEN UND ZURÜCKGLEITEN: Spiele die Note und ziehe wie notiert; lasse den Finger dann in die Ausgangsposition zurückgleiten. Dabei wird nur die erste Note angeschlagen.

ZIEHEN UND NOCHMALIGES ANSCHLAGEN: Spiele die Note und ziehe wie notiert, schlage die Saite neu an, wenn das Symbol "▶" erscheint und lasse den Finger dann zurückgleiten.

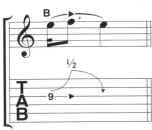

ZIEHER VOR DEM ANSCHLAGEN: Ziehe zuerst die Note wie notiert; schlage die Note dann an.

ZIEHER VOR DEM ANSCHLAGEN MIT ZURÜCKGLEITEN: Ziehe die Note wie notiert; schlage die Note dann an und lasse den Finger auf die Ausgangslage zurückgleiten.

AUFSCHLAGTECHNIK: Schlage die erste (tiefere) Note an; die höhere Note (auf der selben Saite) erklingt durch kräftiges Aufschlagen mit einem anderen Finger der Griffhand.

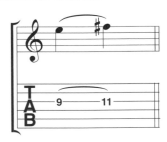

ABZIEHTECHNIK: Setze beide Finger auf die zu spielenden Noten und schlage die erste Note an. Ziehe dann (ohne nochmals anzuschlagen) den oberen Finger der Griffhand seitlich - abwärts ab, um die zweite (tiefere) Note zum klingen zu bringen.

GLISSANDOTECHNIK: Schlage die erste Note an und rutsche dann mit dem selben Finger der Griffhand aufwärts oder abwärts zur zweiten Note. Die zweite Note wird nicht angeschlagen.

GLISSANDOTECHNIK MIT NACHFOLGENDEM ANSCHLAG: Gleiche Technik wie das gebundene Glissando, jedoch wird die zweite Note angeschlagen.

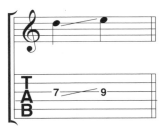

NATÜRLICHES FLAGEOLETT: Berühre die Saite über dem angegebenen Bund leicht mit einem Finger der Griffhand. Schlage die Saite an und lasse sie frei schwingen.

PICK SCRAPE: Fahre mit dem Plektrum nach unten über die Saiten - klappt am besten bei umsponnenen Saiten.

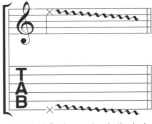

DÄMPFEN MIT DER SCHLAGHAND: Lege die Schlaghand oberhalb der Brücke leicht auf die Saite(n).

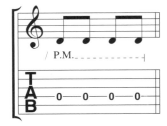

DÄMPFEN MIT DER GRIFFHAND: Du erreichst einen percussiven Sound, indem du die Griffhand leicht über die Saiten legst (ohne diese herunterzudrücken) und dann mit der Schlaghand anschlägst.

AMMERKUNG: Das Tempo der Zieher und Glissandos ist abhängig von der rhythmischen Notation und dem Grundtempo.

Spiegazioni Di Tablatura Per Chitarra

La musica per chitarra può essere annotata in tre diversi modi: sul pentagramma, in tablatura e in taglio ritmico

IL TAGLIO RITMICO è scritto sopra il pentagramma. Percuotere le corde al ritmo indicato Le teste arrotondate delle note indicano note singole.

IL PENTAGRAMMA MUSICALE mostra toni e ritmo ed è divisa da linee in settori. I toni sono indicati con le prime sette lettere dell'alfabeto.

LA TABLATURA rappresenta graficamente la tastiera della chitarra. Ogni linea orizzontale rappresenta una corda, ed ogni corda rappresenta un tasto.

4° corda, 2° tasto   1° e 2° corda aperte, suonate insieme   accordo D aperto

Definizioni Per Annotazioni Speciali Per Chitarra

SEMI-TONO CURVATO: percuotere la nota e curvare di un semitono (1/2 passo).

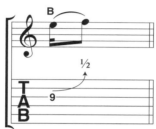

TONO CURVATO: Percuotere la nota e curvare di un tono (passo intero).

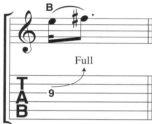

NOTA BREVE, CURVATA: percuotere la nota e curvare come indicato. Suonare la prima nota il più velocemente possibile.

QUARTO DI TONO, CURVATO: Percuotere la nota e curvare di un quarto di passo.

CURVA E LASCIA: Percuotere la nota e curvare come indicato, quindi rilasciare indietro alla nota originale.

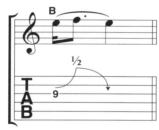

CURVA E RIPERCUOTI: Percuotere la nota e curvare come indicato poi ripercuotere la corda nel punto del simbolo.

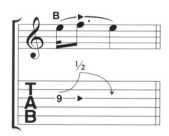

PRE-CURVA: Curvare la nota come indicato e quindi percuoterla.

PRE-CURVA E RILASCIO: Curvare la nota come indicato. Colpire e rilasciare la nota indietro alla tonalità indicata.

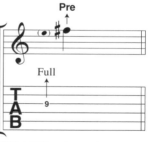

MARTELLO-COLPISCI: Colpire la prima nota (in basso) con un dito; quindi suona la nota più alta (sulla stessa corda) con un altro dito, toccandola senza pizzicare.

TOGLIERE: Posizionare entrambe le dita sulla nota da suonare. Colpire la prima nota e, senza pizzicare, togliere le dita per suonare la seconda nota (più in basso).

LEGATO SCIVOLATO (GLISSATO): Colpire la prima nota e quindi far scivolare lo stesso dito della mano della tastiera su o giù alla seconda nota. La seconda nota non viene colpita.

CAMBIO SCIVOLATO (GLISSARE E RICOLPIRE): Uguale al legato - scivolato eccetto che viene colpita la seconda nota.

ARMONICA NATURALE: Colpire la nota mentre la mano della tastiera tocca leggermente la corda direttamente sopra il tasto indicato.

PIZZICA E GRAFFIA: Il limite del pizzicato è tirato su (o giù) lungo la corda, producendo un suono graffiante.

SORDINA CON IL PALMO: La nota è parzialmente attenuata dalla mano del pizzicato toccando la corda (le corde) appena prima del ponte.

CORDE SMORZATE: Un suono di percussione viene prodotto appoggiando la mano della tastiera attraverso la corda (le corde) senza premere, e colpendole con la mano del pizzicato.

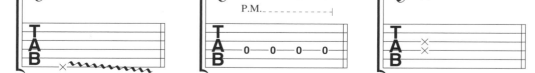

NOTA: La velocità di ogni curvatura è indicata dalle annotazioni musicali e dal tempo.

Tablatura De Guitarra Explicada

La música de guitarra puede ser representada en tres formas diferentes: en un pentagrama, en tablatura, y con acentos rítmicos.

ACENTOS RITMICOS están escritos sobre el pentagrama. Rasguea los acordes cuando te indique los acentos rítmicos. La aparición de una nota rodeada por un círculo indica una sola nota.

EL PENTAGRAMA muestra la altura y el ritmo y está dividida en compases mediante unas líneas. La altura de las notas se denominan con las siete primeras notas del alfabeto.

TABLATURA representa gráficamente el diapasón de la guitarra. Cada línea horizontal representa una cuerda, y cada número representa un traste.

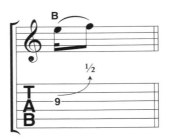

4ª Cuerda, 2º traste · 1ª y 2ª cuerda al aire, tocadas a la vez · Acorde de D abierto

Definiciones Especiales Para La Notacion De Guitarra

BEND DE UN SEMITONO : Ataca la nota y eleva la cuerda hasta que esté medio tono por encima de la nota original (1/2 tono).

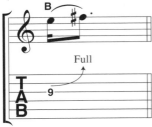

BEND DE UN TONO : Ataca la nota y eleva de la cuerda hasta que esté un tono por encima de la original (un tono completo).

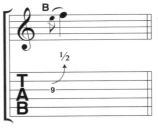

BEND DE UNA NOTA RAPIDA (GRACE NOTE) : Ataca la nota y eleva la cuerda según se indique en la tablatura. Toca la primera nota tan rápidamente como te sea posible.

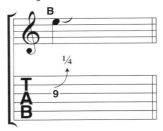

BEND DE UN CUARTO DE TONO : Ataca la nota y eleva la cuerda hasta que esté un cuarto de tono (1/4 tono) por encima de la original.

BEND & RELEASE : Ataca la nota y eleva la cuerda según se indica en la tablatura, regresa a la posición y nota iniciales.

BEND & RESTRIKE: : Ataca la nota y eleva la cuerda según lo que indicado entonces ataca de nuevo la cuerda en la que aparece el símbolo.

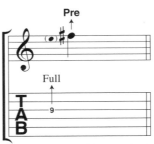

PRE-BEND : Eleva la cuerda según lo indicado, después atácala.

PRE-BEND & RELEASE : Eleva la cuerda según lo indicado. Atácala y regresa a la posición y nota original.

HAMMER-ON : Ataca una nota (grave) con un dedo, entonces haz sonar otra nota más aguda (en la misma cuerda) con otro dedo al tocarla directamente sobre el diapasón, sin atacar la cuerda de nuevo con la púa o los dedos.

PULL-OFF: Sitúa los dedos sobre las notas que desees hacer sonar. Ataca la primera nota y sin utilizar la púa (o los dedos), retira el dedo para hacer que la segunda nota (más grave) suene.

LEGATO SLIDE (GLISS) : Ataca la primera nota y entonces desliza el mismo dedo de la mano situada sobre el diapasón de forma ascendente o descendente hasta alcanzar la segunda nota. La segunda nota no se produce al ser atacada por los dedos o la púa.

SHIFT SLIDE (GLISS & RESTRIKE): Igual que el legato slide, excepto que la segunda nota se ataca con la púa o los dedos.

ARMÓNICOS NATURALES : Ataca la nota mientras que la mano situada sobre el diapasón roza ligeramente la cuerda directamente sobre el traste indicado.

RASPADO DE PÚA : El borde de la púa se desliza de forma descendente (o ascendente) por las cuerdas, provocando un sonido rasposo.

PALM MUTING : La nota es parcialmente apagada al apoyar la mano de la púa ligeramente sobre la cuerdas situándola justo antes del puente.

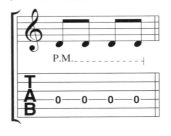

CUERDAS APAGADAS : Un sonido percusivo que se consigue al apoyar la mano situada sobre el diapasón sobre las cuerda (s) relajando la presión sobre éste, mientras que se ataca (n) con la otra mano.

NOTA : La velocidad de cualquier bend está indicada por la notación musical y el tempo.

Printed in Malta by Interprint Limited

10/04 (52806)